managing editor: Maddalena Paola Winspeare
graphic design: Laura Belforte
editing: Giulia Bastianelli
translation: Anthony Cafazzo
drawings on pages 21, 29, 35, 36, 37, 53, 54: Susanna Coseschi

reproduction rights: Archivio Sillabe: Foto Paolo Nannoni, Foto Antonio Quattrone, Foto Rabatti & Domingie, Foto Sara Zinelli. Firenze, Museo "Firenze com'era"; Opera di Santa Maria del Fiore; Soprintendenza per i Beni Ambientali e per il Patrimonio Storico, Artistico e Demoetnoantropologico di Firenze, Pistoia e Prato; Soprintendenza Speciale per il Polo Museale Fiorentino; Comune di Scarperia. Milano, Biblioteca Ambrosiana

Roberto Corazzi made the drawings on pages 1, 37, 38 (low), 43, 44, 51, 55, 59, 60 and on cover

The publisher is at the disposal of the copyright holders of images from unidentified sources

acknowledgements:
The authors wish to thank architect Stefania Marini for her invaluable collaboration on the historical research, as well as surveyor Paolo Bianchini and the staff of the Opera di Santa Maria del Fiore for their support in conducting the technological research on the Cupola

ISBN 88-8347-248-9

Giuseppe Conti
Roberto Corazzi

The Cupola of Santa Maria del Fiore

as told by its creator

Filippo Brunelleschi

sillabe

From 1420 to 1436 Florence saw the realisation of an unrivalled feat of architecture: the Dome of the Cathedral of Santa Maria del Fiore, which rose imposingly to cast its shadow over the city centre's homes and shops. The original plans to cover the Cathedral, conceived of more than a full century earlier by its architect Arnolfo di Cambio, called for a much smaller dome, but it was Filippo Brunelleschi's far more ambitious design that was to become the very symbol of this city and the eternal pride of its citizens.

Today, almost six centuries later, this book's authors have brought Brunelleschi back to life to have him narrate his adventure and help us understand his life and times – a time when great cathedrals were built, and men of genius invented that which was destined to become the Renaissance.

We therefore owe a debt of gratitude to Conti and Corazzi for these, their writings, which in a clear narrative style has enabled Brunelleschi himself to lead us along the path of discovery through the world handed down to us in the great works that have made Florence a treasure chest of art – the patrimony of all mankind.

Anna Mitrano

President of Opera di Santa Maria del Fiore

5

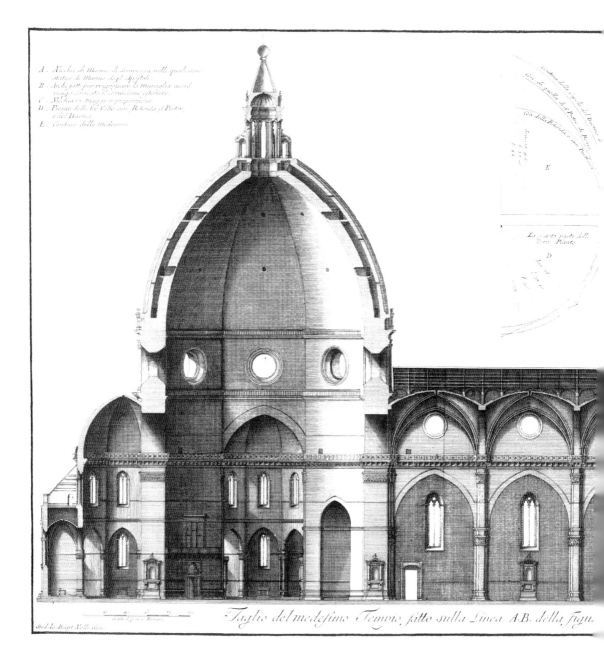

Scala di piedi Romani

Stud: L. Bapt: Nelli 1601.

Taglio del medesimo Tempio, fatto sulla Linea A.B. della figu.

Contents

Introduction   8

Chapter 1. The history of the Cathedral

1.1   A brief history of the Cathedral

        and Arnolfo di Cambio's design   11

1.2   The rivalry with Siena

        and expansion of the Cathedral   16

1.3   The eve of the great undertaking   18

1.4   The contest for the Dome commission   27

Chapter 2. Building the Dome

2.1   The adventure begins   33

2.2   How I created my masterpiece   36

2.3   The Dome and mathematics   42

2.4   Within the Cupola   48

Biography of Filippo Brunelleschi   56

Glossary of the Cupola   58

Bibliography   62

Introduction

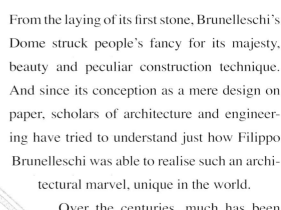

From the laying of its first stone, Brunelleschi's Dome struck people's fancy for its majesty, beauty and peculiar construction technique. And since its conception as a mere design on paper, scholars of architecture and engineering have tried to understand just how Filippo Brunelleschi was able to realise such an architectural marvel, unique in the world.

Over the centuries, much has been written about the Dome, both in scientific journals and in the popular press, but most is comprehensible only to those 'initiated' in the sciences of architecture and engineering. Although a number of attempts have been made to explain the Dome and its construction in simple terms, none do justice to its geometrical complexities or the revolutionary building techniques used to erect it. Two reasons underlie such failure: firstly, only recently have researchers been able to unveil the 'secrets' of the building methods developed by Brunelleschi, and secondly, the geometrical and technical concepts underlying any adequate explanation are simply quite complex. One further confounding factor is that, for reasons explained in this book, Brunelleschi never fully revealed just how he realised his masterpiece.

The book's authors have spent years thoroughly studying the renowned monument, using the most modern techniques. Their painstaking research, coupled with careful study of the contributions of all those scholars who have gone before them, has enabled them to reveal the basic principles that guided Brunelleschi in constructing "his Dome", to unlock its secrets and grasp several aspects that had, until now, remained obscure. Many of these findings have been included in this book.

In order to help the reader better understand the history of the Dome's building, its structure, geometry and the techniques adopted, the authors have written this book in the form of a first-hand account by Brunelleschi himself. The resulting chronicle is a captivating adventure into the history of the Dome, immediate and simple, yet scientifically rigorous. A number of curious, at times humorous, though always historically faithful anecdotes serve to bring the story to life. And to further clarify it, the narrative has been illustrated through numerous photographs and drawings.

A glossary has also been included to explain the technical terms used in the book – the first occurrence of each of these terms is indicated in **bold type** in the text. Finally, a brief, but exhaustive biography of Brunelleschi will help the reader understand the unfolding of the historical events described. Step by step, the reader will be brought to understand the most recondite secrets of the Dome and its history.

We hope you will find it not only informative, but above all, enjoyable!

The Authors

1
The history of the Cathedral

A brief history of the Cathedral and Arnolfo di Cambio's design

Andrea di Lazzaro da Buggiano, *Bust of Filippo Brunelleschi*, Florence, Santa Maria del Fiore

Hello! My name is Filippo Brunelleschi.

I was born in Florence in 1377 and I am an architect by trade, even if I started out my artistic career as a goldsmith. I am sure you will understand the reasons for my career choice soon enough, but for the moment let me tell you about the work I am proudest of (and most famous for): the Cupola of the Cathedral of Santa Maria del Fiore in Florence.

Would you like to know more about this marvellous construction? Don't be afraid, come closer. Although I am known to have a bad temper, I'd like to be your friend. Here, just to show you that I come in peace, I extend you my right hand, so I can grip yours. According to a medieval Florentine custom, this shows that I am not hiding any weapons. Yes, just like that! You see, my fellow citizens were a very quarrelsome lot: brawls were an everyday occurrence, and more often than not someone would produce a weapon. However, there is some justification for the Florentines' rather belligerent behaviour: their main activity was commerce, so they travelled far and wide, and in those times travelling was very dangerous indeed. One always had to be armed and ready to defend oneself from brigands.

Through commerce the Florentines accumulated enormous riches. Each and every merchant family desired to show the world that it was the wealthiest and most powerful of all. However, if everyone wants to be number one, it is only natural that fierce disputes will break out: in fact, the history of my city is full of such episodes. Nonetheless, all Florentines loved their city dearly (they called it "Fiorenza", which means flower) and wanted it to be the most beautiful of all.

Thus, they filled it with palaces, churches and arcades. In the early 15th century, when I was just a promising young goldsmith, my city was filled with those great artists whose works have

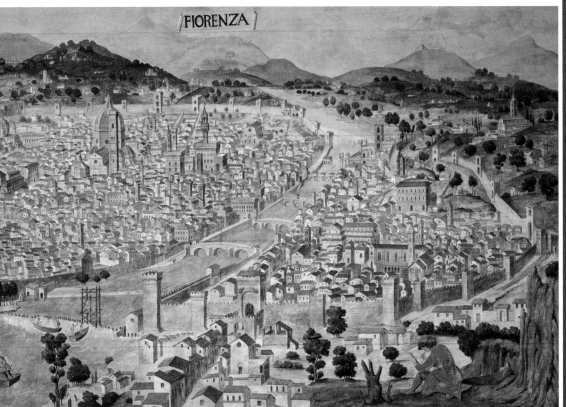

made Florence so famous. At the time, money abounded in Florence and, fortunately, so did good artists. It was the beginning of that period that historians would eventually call the "Renaissance" (which means rebirth). In all modesty, I myself have made a beautiful contribution to this artistic period, unique in the history of Man! This time of splendour had already lasted

Francesco di Lorenzo Rosselli, Prospect of the 'Wooden Chain' (19th-century copy), Florence, Museum of "Firenze com'era"

Miniature: two cloth merchants

nearly a full century when I was born, to be exact on September 8th 1296. But let's go back a bit. Just about 80 years before my hand, the first stone of the new Florence Cathedral had been laid. This "Duomo", as Italians still call a cathedral, was designed by the greatest architect of the time, Arnolfo di Cambio.

At the time other beautiful city churches were being built in Florence, such as for instance, Santa Croce (Church of the Holy Cross, also designed by di Cambio) and Santa Maria Novella.

Many were the sins for which the Florentines needed forgiveness, and thus they sought to obtain God's indulgence by contributing to the construction of these churches. The Church of Santa Maria Novella still bears a fresco showing the Cathedral as di Cambio originally planned it: it is found in the cloister, in the so-called Chapel of the Spaniards (*Cappellone degli Spagnoli*). As you can see, he had planned a cupola, or dome, with an octagonal base, similar in shape to the one I would build about 120 years later, but smaller: in fact it was originally supposed to measure about 36 meters across; mine instead is 45 meters.

John B. Philpot, *The Church of Santa Croce, Florence*, photograph (pre-1857), Florence, Gabinetto Fotografico della Soprintendenza Speciale per il Polo Museale Fiorentino

Giuseppe and Vittorio Jaquier, *The Church of Santa Maria Novella*, photograph (c. 1890), Florence, Gabinetto Fotografico della Soprintendenza Speciale per il Polo Museale Fiorentino

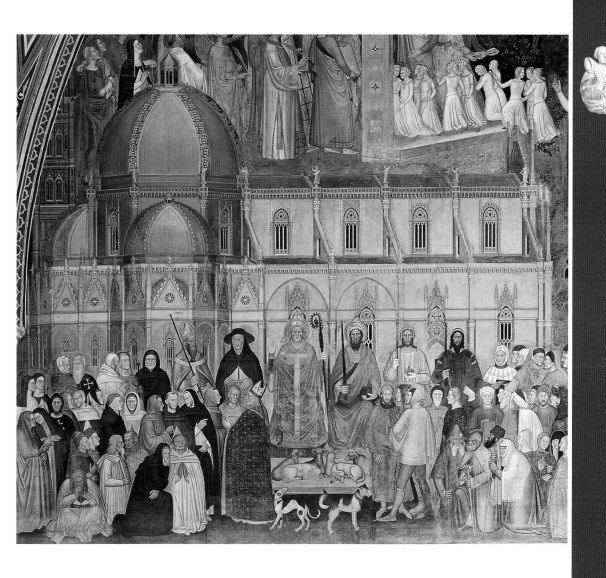

Andrea di Bonaiuto, *The triumphant Church* (1367-1369),
detail of the Cathedral of Santa Maria del Fiore by Arnolfo
di Cambio, Florence, Cloister of Santa Maria Novella

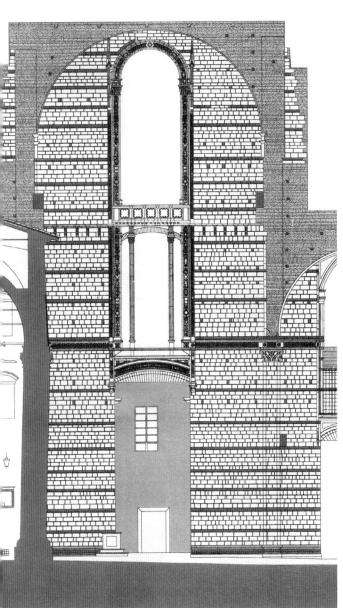

You may ask why the final Dome was made larger than the original plan. You see, the vanity of my fellow citizens knew no limits. Thus, when they decided to build the new cathedral, they wanted it to be the greatest and most beautiful church in all Christendom. The city folk of Siena, Florence's chief, though not only rival, learnt of the plan for the new cathedral and decided to outdo the Florentines by enlarging their own. In the end, they outdid even themselves, because they made it so big that at a certain point the structure just did not hold up: the walls gave in and the site was abandoned. To this day, the Piazza del Duomo in Siena contains the remains of what was supposed to be the extension.

Meanwhile, the Florentines, not to be out-shone by their archrivals of Siena, decided to plan an even larger cathedral.

As usual, there was a great deal of contention surrounding the new plan. As was their wont, the Florentines were divided into two factions. Eventually, in 1367, the faction to which my father belonged won out. Indeed, my father, the wealthy notary, Ser Brunellesco di Lippo Lapi, had participated in the debate over the Cathedral. This was surely the hand of fate.

The new design called for a cupola, still octagonal at its base, but measuring 45 meters across on the inside, as I have already mentioned. Furthermore, a 13-meter high **drum** or **tambour** (the masonry structure below the dome with the round windows called 'lunettes') was to be added. This drum was not part of di Cambio's original design and its presence made building the Dome more problematic, as it would now have to be constructed starting at a height of almost 55 meters above the ground! It would have been far easier to build the Dome if the Cathedral's original design had been followed. But perhaps it was for the best, because in this way, I had the chance to create something everyone thought was impossible!

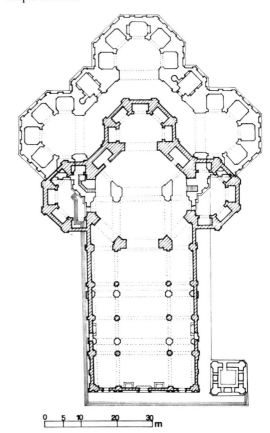

17

Survey of the counter-façade of the Duomo Nuovo in Siena (from S. Eusepi - G. Grisanti)

Arnolfo di Cambio's designs for the Cathedral of Santa Maria del Fiore superimposed with the plans for its subsequent expansion

1.3

The eve of the great undertaking

I have already insinuated that it was my fate to build the Dome. In fact, I grew up next to the Cathedral square and thus had the privilege of watching the stonemasons working on its construction. I saw the machines used to lift the marble and stone blocks, and was left in awe. I always loved mechanical things and, strange as it may seem, that is why I decided to become a goldsmith. You see, in my times goldsmiths not only made jewellery, but also built clocks, so I decided to begin an apprenticeship in the shop of the goldsmith, Benincasa Lotti, a friend of my family's. There, my training embraced many fields of knowledge. I was taught that in order to smelt gold, you needed to add copper, bronze, lead and sulphur, then I learnt to make the clay casts into which these materials were poured. In short, I had to know much of that discipline that today you call chemistry.

Such knowledge came in very useful in build-

ing the Cupola: in fact, they gave me a deep understanding of the materials – the mortar, stones, clay and metals – with which I was to forge the iron **brackets** used to hold together the masonry elements (stones and bricks).

By building clocks, I also learnt much about the modern discipline of mechanics. I built many clocks in my time, but only one has survived: you can see it in the building called *Palazzo dei Vicari* in Scarperia, a town not far from Florence.

My knowledge of mechanics also proved to be very useful: in fact, I eventually designed the machines that the workers used to lift the necessary building materials up to the Dome. Their functioning depended on complex systems of wheels, gears, screws, counterweights, and so forth.

These marvellous machines that I had designed remained at the Cathedral building site even after I died in 1446. They were used afterwards, especially to build the **Lantern,** that smaller cylindrical structure on top of the Dome, which I planned as well.

In 1472 Verrocchio built a bronze ball 2.5 meters in diameter. It was set on top of the Lantern, still using my machines. Among the

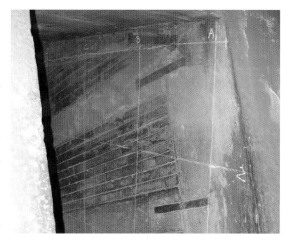

Circle of Bernardo Daddi, *Madonna of Mercy*, Florence, Museum of the Bigallo

View of the iron brackets fastening the Dome's stone blocks

Filippo Brunelleschi, Clockworks (15th century), Scarperia, Palazzo dei Vicari

'shop boys' who helped Verrocchio in this difficult operation, was a young man by the name of Leonardo, from the nearby town of Vinci. He studiously made notes and drawings of my devices: I can therefore rightfully boast that I served as inspiration for Leonardo da Vinci in his planning of some of the many machines for which he is famous.

I was also very good at mathematics. I furnished proof of this ability of mine by carrying out an experiment in perspective, to which I applied some fundamental laws of geometry. I made an ingenious painting of the Florence Baptistery on a small wooden panel by applying geometric rules of perspective that I myself discovered. What I did was this… I made a small hole in the panel, at

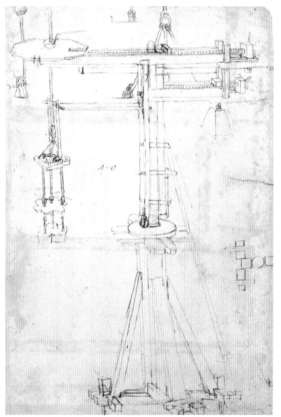

what today is called 'the vanishing point'. Looking at it from the back, observers would see the image of the Baptistery reflected on a mirror positioned in front of the panel at just the right distance. Instead, an observer standing at the door of the Cathedral would get the impression of seeing the real Baptistery, when it was actually only an image reflected in the mirror!

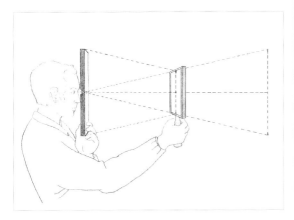

Leonardo da Vinci, Brunelleschi's revolving crane (1478-1519), Milan, Ambrosiana Library

View of the Lantern of the Dome

Diagram of the optical principles on which Brunelleshi based his panel of the Florence Baptistery

Masaccio, *Holy Trinity* (c. 1427), Florence, Santa Maria Novella

That panel has unfortunately been lost. Nevertheless, you can get an idea of my mathematical skill in applying the laws of perspective by observing the *Trinità* (*Holy Trinity*), which my friend Masaccio painted in 1427 on the left wall of the Church of Santa Maria Novella.

It was I who executed the perspective framework for this fresco. As you can see, the laws of geometry have been applied rigorously, in such way as to achieve splendid scenographic effects and a sense of depth that only perspective is able to confer.

A goldsmith must be an artist to make jewellery. I managed to develop great skill in this field as well, and in 1398 I became a master goldsmith. Then in 1401 I took part in a competition: the winner would be given the commission to create the bronze doors for the city Baptistery. Each candidate had one year to create a decorated panel. At the outset, there were seven of us; at the end, only two: myself and a theretofore unknown goldsmith by the name of Lorenzo Ghiberti. We both had made a panel of "The Sacrifice of Isaac". I shall let you judge for yourselves which is the more beautiful!

The 34 members of the jury could not make up

their minds and, predictably, two factions formed (the Florentines will never change!). In the end, Lorenzo Ghiberti won out; but to this day I still maintain that there were some irregularities and favouritism in his favour. As I shall recount presently, I would eventually get my revenge on Lorenzo, but only many years later. Meanwhile, a great rivalry was established between the two cible than I was! I told no one the reason for this journey, though in fact I had learnt that within a few years construction of the Florence Cathedral Dome was to commence. This was an event I wanted to be ready for. The city of Rome was still replete with the remnants of ancient Roman architecture, and I fervently wished to discover the secrets of those marvel-

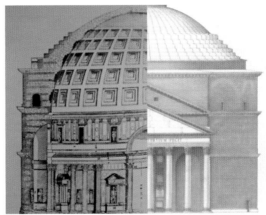

of us, one which was to last our lifetime.

Disappointed by the contest's results, after a time I gave the panel to Cosimo de' Medici and departed for Rome with my dear friend Donatello, the famous sculptor. We two got along very well together, perhaps because we both had the same sort of temperament. To be honest, Donatello was even more iras-

Lorenzo Ghiberti, *The Sacrifice of Isaac*, Florence, Museum of the Bargello

Filippo Brunelleschi, *The Sacrifice of Isaac*, Florence, Museum of the Bargello

Giovan Battista Piranesi, Interior view of the Pantheon

Façade and cross section of the Pantheon

lous structures. Thus, I went to Rome several times in the period between 1402 and 1416.

In addition, there was a cupola in Rome whose dimensions were similar to the one that I would have to build: the dome of the Pantheon.

The Pantheon had been built under the Emperor Hadrian, between 118 and 128 AD. It has a hemisphere-shaped cupola about 43.20 meters in diameter. Thus, it was quite close in size to the one I would build in Florence – as I have already told you, the base of my Dome is an octagon measuring 77 'arms' across on the inside (that is about 45 meters, the length of a Florentine arm being about 0.5836 meters).

However, while the Pantheon's base is a circle, that of my Dome is a regular octagon (well, nearly so). As I shall explain later, building a dome with a polygon-shaped base presents rather more complex problems than a circular base. In fact, as you will see, this was one of the greatest difficul-

24

Venetian masters, Cupola mosaics, Florence Baptistery
View of the Florence Baptistery

Venetian masters, Detail of the Cupola mosaics, Florence, Baptistery

Cross-sectional comparison of the domes of Santa Maria del Fiore, the Pantheon and the Florence Baptistery

ties I encountered in constructing my Dome.

At this point you will ask why an octagonal-based cupola was chosen for the Cathedral in Florence. Well, you see the reason lies mainly in tradition: when di Cambio chose a shape for the Dome, he was inspired by the Florence Baptistery, which contains an interior octagonal cupola, with a diameter of about 28 meters. The Church of the Baptistery has always been very dear to the Florentines: Dante Alighieri, who was baptised there, called it "il mio bel San Giovanni" (my beautiful Saint John). The interior walls of its cupola are adorned with splendid mosaics.

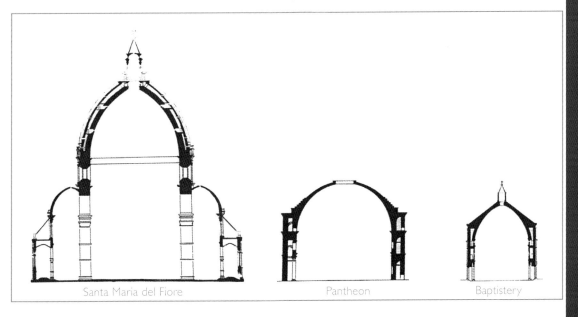

Santa Maria del Fiore   Pantheon   Baptistery

I had also planned to have the interior surface of my Dome covered with mosaics, but about 150 years later, the Florentines decided instead to paint some frescoes depicting *The Last Judgment*.

However, this was no easy enterprise either. The eight wedge-shaped segments (called **webs** or **cells**) that form the inner dome make up a total surface area of about 3,600 square meters. Moreover, as I am sure you can imagine, it is no easy task to work at such a height. Fortunately, I had also foreseen this and inserted numerous iron rings into the Cupola's walls: these would serve as supports for the scaffolding on which the frescoes' authors were to work (Vasari and Zuccari). In fact, that is exactly what they did.

One of the iron rings fitted by Brunelleschi onto the Cupola to support the scaffolding used for decorating its interior surface

Giorgio Vasari and Federico Zuccari, *The Last Judgement*, Florence, Santa Maria del Fiore

Filippo Brunelleschi, *Wooden model for the Cupola of Santa Maria del Fiore, Florence*, Museum of the Opera di Santa Maria del Fiore

The contest for the Dome commission

In August 1418 the *Opera del Duomo* (the cathedral management authority) called a competition to determine who would build the Dome. I had definitively returned from Rome and was anxious to compete for this great honour. Twelve projects were entered. In the end, after a good deal of wavering, the jury concentrated on two projects: mine and (would you believe it?) Lorenzo Ghiberti's! Him again! just as in the contest for the Baptistery doors 17 years earlier. History was repeating itself!

And once again the jury was unable to come to a decision. Lorenzo and I had both built a masonry model of our proposal. With the help of my dear friend Donatello, I had built one of brick, with the extra advantage that the jury members could examine it from within as well, as it was two meters wide and four

high. This model was eventually destroyed, but the Museum of the *Opera del Duomo* still holds another, wooden model which I made myself as well.

The most common method of building an octagonal dome was to use **centring**. Centring is a temporary wooden framework that has the same shape as a dome or arch under construction. The method is very simple: the bricks are laid using the centring as the supporting structure. After the arch or dome is finished, the framework can be dismantled, as the masonry structure is now able to support itself!

This method had been used for ages. However, when building a hemispherical cupola, or more in general, a **circular** or **rotating dome**, it can be completed without the cen-tred framework: one need only lay concentric rings of bricks in successive layers. These support each other, and the growing dome can stand alone. In mechanical terms, such a structure is said to be self-supporting.

Controlling the masonry's geometry is performed with a long rod or wire, one end of which is set in the sphere's centre. This also serves as a guide to determine the slope of the bricks, which are laid along the **parallels** of the sphere.

While a circle is a perfect figure, an octagon is not. Circles have no angles, the octagon instead does. In domes with circular bases, the forces bearing down on the structure are distributed equally; in octagonal ones, this is not the case. This was another reason why, during my discussions with the jury members before the Dome's construction, I proposed

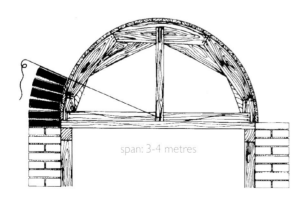

span: 3-4 metres

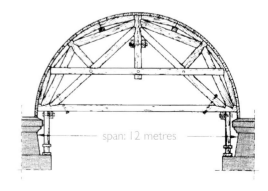

span: 12 metres

substituting the octagonal base of the dome with a circular one and thereafter building a rotating dome. But, out of respect for tradition, the members of the *Opera del Duomo* rejected this proposal. Another factor in their decision was that the drum had already been built in the shape of an octagon, and it would have been a difficult undertaking to design a circular-based dome to fit over it.

In conclusion, the only way to erect our dome was to use a wooden centred framework. However, this method revealed to be impracticable right from the start. If we wanted to build using traditional techniques, we would have needed a wooden framework about 32 meters high, set up at a height of almost 55 meters from the ground. Moreover, the wooden centring would have had to support enormous weight during the long years of construction. Indeed, the Cupola weighs about 27,000 tons (as much as one of your modern transatlantic ships!) and took 16 years to build! The whole enterprise looked impossible and, to make matters worse, such a wooden structure would cost a fortune (a fact that, in the end, played in my favour, as we shall see).

One of the other designs entered into the competition called for using, instead of a centred framework, a 90-meter high mountain of earth! This method was often used for building **vaults** or domes, but their heights had to be kept within reasonable limits – in our case, such a system was absolutely unsuitable. If the dome to be built had conformed to the dimensions foreseen by di Cambio in his

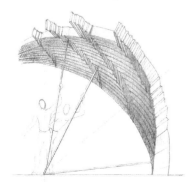

Techniques for building an arch with the support of a wooden centring framework

Technique for building a circular dome with the aid of a guide rod original design, everything would have been far simpler, amongst other reasons, because the lighter dome would produce less stress on the whole structure. But this behemoth of a Cupola! Both its size and shape complicated everything!

At the time, I wondered if those who had planned to enlarge the Cathedral had any idea of the difficulties involved in building an octagonal dome of such dimensions! Now I am quite certain that they did, but I am equally certain that they also knew that they would not be the ones who would have to build it! Perhaps they thought that their successors would invent techniques suitable to the task. This was, in effect, how it turned out, but I doubt they ever imagined there would be one sole architect able to pull it off – me!

In order to overcome all the difficulties that I have explained up to now, I proposed a revolutionary design: I would build the Dome without centring! Despite its octagonal base, I would erect it without any supporting frame, as if it were a circular dome. How did I do it? That, I shall come to presently. The design that I proposed was a completely

new and seemingly impossible one. In fact, when I told of my idea, everybody thought I was mad. At the meeting held to discuss it, I often had to be dragged out of the room, as if I were out of my head! During one of these discussions, some asked me to lay out my plans. Having no intention of revealing anything of the sort, I challenged those present to set an egg down on a marble table and leave it standing on end. All tried, but none succeeded. Then I took the egg and, tapping it lightly on the table, dented its lower portion. Needless to say, the egg stood upright. Those present protested vehemently, and I laughingly replied that once I showed them my model or drawings, they would understand how to build the dome just as they now knew how to stand an egg on end!

This anecdote became famous and was later attributed to a certain Christopher Columbus, from Genoa, who like I, was also considered mad when he proposed the journey that eventually led to the discovery of America. For this reason, the anecdote is known as "Columbus' egg", but I thought of it first, and a long time before he did. Speaking of Christopher Columbus, I should tell you that the idea for his famous journey came to him when he acquired maps compiled by the great Florentine mathematician, Paolo Toscanelli, a dear friend of mine. Mapmaking required studying the stars, and in my times there were no telescopes. So to carry out his astronomical observations, Paolo set a metal ring in a hole on my Dome, at the base of the Lantern. Every summer solstice the light of the sun passes through this aperture and illuminates a disk set inside the Cathedral, near the base of the Dome.

Such an apparatus is called a gnomon and still today the phenomenon can be witnessed during the summer solstice. In this way, Paolo was able to study the Earth's orbit and make more precise maps, which Columbus and Vespucci also used. for their journeys.

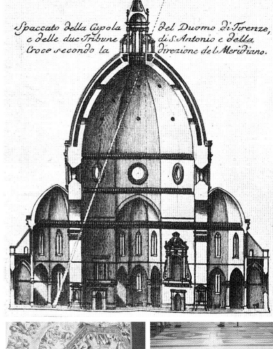

Spaccato della Cupola e delle due Tribune Croce secondo la / del Duomo di Firenze, di S. Antonio e della Direzione del Meridiano.

Leonardo Ximenes, Transverse section of the Cupola showing sunlight entering through the bearing brass at the Lantern's base
Beginning of the sun's passage on June 21st (summer solstice)
View of the sundial on the Cathedral transept floor before the Chapel of the Cross

2
Building
the
Dome

2.1
The adventure begins

Eventually, in 1420, the jury decided to name Lorenzo Ghiberti, a certain Battista d'Antonio and yours truly 'capomastri' (that is, taskmasters or superintendents) of the Cupola. You see, the Florentines did not trust me much, so they assigned these two colleagues to keep an eye on me. At first, I was very angry at the presence of these two, whom I viewed as intruders, especially Lorenzo, and I wanted to abandon the enterprise altogether. Then I reconsidered: after all, I had won; the design to be executed was mine; I and only I held the title of "inventor and governor of the great cupola".

You will be asking yourselves why my design had won out over the others. The answer is simple: because it was the only one that could actually be built. The Florentines realised that only by following my plan could the Dome be erected. It was also the most economical, since I had dispensed with construction of the expensive centred wooden framework. Actually, this was likely the most important reason for my fellow citizens, who were very close with money! (On the other hand, without such closeness, they never would have accumulated such wealth now, would they?) Also, I must admit that I was certain that I could quickly rid myself of Lorenzo by revealing his incompetence in architecture.

In April 1420, the other taskmasters and I presented the programme for construction of the Cupola. Eventually, it was to be revised twice, once in 1422 and then again in 1426. The report detailed the Dome's technical characteristics, but it did not explain the methods to be used for its actual construction. My reasoning remained the same: after so many sacrifices and so many struggles, I had no intention of allowing others to steal my ideas. I would make sure that I, and I alone knew how to manage the operations of building what I was already thinking of as "my Dome".

Soon the moment came to get my revenge on Lorenzo Ghiberti. Would you like to know just how I did it? Well here you have it. In late 1423 I faked a serious illness. My playacting was so good that people actually began thinking that I was on my deathbed. Responsibility for the construction fell on Lorenzo, who quickly revealed to be incapable of carrying on the work. At this point, as if by miracle, I recovered and began a campaign of criticism against Lorenzo. The *Opera del Duomo* finally realised that only I could carry out the design. Lorenzo went without salary for eight months, but was then reinstated at 36 florins per year. My salary was instead raised to 100 florins (an enormous figure in those days): they had finally come to understand that I was far more important than he. But what a dreadful prank to play on poor Lorenzo!

Speaking of which, I have always loved pranks. A few years earlier, in 1409, I organised a practical joke on a carpenter named Manetto, who we all knew as "fat jack", in return for a number of wrongs he had done me. In cahoots with others, I managed to make him believe that he was some other person. It went off so well that Manetto actually believed he was somebody else!

In 1426 the Cupola reached the height of almost 12 meters, and we started on the curved portions of the structure: the most difficult and dangerous part had begun!

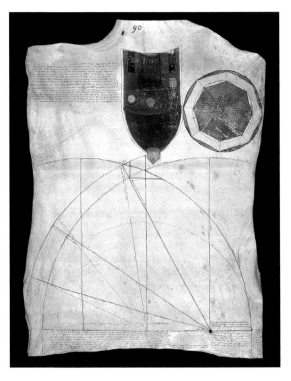

An assistant of Lorenzo Ghiberti's, a certain Giovanni di Gherardo da Prato, wrote in a parchment that I was wholly mistaken and that the Dome would collapse. "Think of the dis-

Parchment by Giovanni di Gherardo da Prato (c. 1424), Florence, Archivio di Stato, Opera di Firenze, 90

Hypothetical location and arrangement of the first ring of stones

Perspective cutaway with hypothetical reconstruction of the scaffoldings conceived by Brunelleschi for construction of the Dome

aster that befell Siena's Cathedral!", exhorted Giovanni. Of course, how could he write otherwise? He was a friend of Lorenzo's.

For my good fortune (and, perhaps, the misfortune of my enemies), the Cupola did not collapse, and the work continued up to 1436, when construction was completed (except for the Lantern).

During all those years, only one fatal accident occurred: in 1422 a stonemason fell from the scaffolding. He may have been a bit inebriated, and so I ordered that from then on only watered-down wine be served to the workers. Unfortunately, I could not give them only water to drink, as I would have liked: the wine served to disinfect the water. Even in those times there was a serious water pollution problem due to all the toxic waste that the wool industry (one of Florence's greatest sources of wealth) discharged in the Arno River. So you see, yours is not the only era to have such problems. Thanks to this and other expedients, not to mention the **scaffolding** that I had designed (on which the masons worked in extreme safety), there were no more fatal accidents.

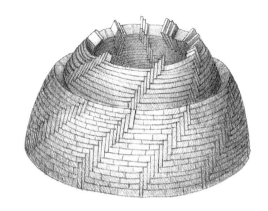

2.2

How I created my masterpiece

Now let us have a look at the building technique and technical means that allowed me to erect the Dome, without centring, of course. I have already told you that the simplest domes to build are circular ones. In fact, they can be erected without a centred framework: one need only lay concentric rings of bricks (parallels) one layer after the other, and they are self-supporting. However, there is one small drawback: as the structure gets higher, the bricks become more and more inclined. When this sloping becomes excessive, the bricks can slide inward and downward before the mortar binding them has a chance to solidify. To prevent this slippage, some bricks are set 'knife-edged', that is vertically, with their long sides perpendicular to the parallels.

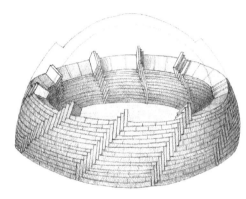

Axonometric view of two spherical domes

Axonometric view of a portion of a spherical dome showing the brickwork

Section of spherical dome showing the brickwork

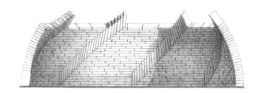

These stop the bricks along the parallels from sliding until the mortar hardens. It is much like adding many small arches, which eventually form a complete circular ring (the parallel).

This arrangement is called a **herringbone** brick pattern, because the bricks are arranged like the bones of a fish. It is an ingenious method, once used by Islamic architects, who learnt it from the Byzantines, who in turn probably learnt it from the ancient Romans. In my times, this technique was not widespread in the West, while in the East it was instead often used to build circular domes.

As I have already said, my Dome is not circular. In fact, its base is an octagon. Just the same, I used the 'herringbone' arrangement of the bricks in my Dome with the same function as in circular domes.

I came up with a revolutionary idea: I applied a technique typical of circular domes to one with an octagonal base! The bricks making up the 'herringbone' follow

Part of the brickwork of the inner cupola exposed during restorations

Cylindrical helix

Frontal and plane view showing the arrangement of cylindrical helices on the dome's webs

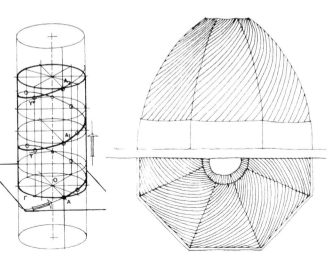

a curve similar to that of spiral staircases, termed a **cylindrical helix**.

But this is not the only technique typical of circular domes that I applied to my Dome. As you will remember, in circular domes the bricks are arranged along rings – the parallels – termed so because they lie on a plane horizontal to the earth. The meridians, on the other hand, are the lines that form right angles with the parallels, just as on the Earth's surface.

In circular domes the bricks, which are arranged along the parallels, are tilted toward the centre of the sphere. Thus, they lie on special surfaces: these are no more than simple **cones** with vertices at the sphere's centre.

I have said a number of times that my Dome has an octagonal base. Now, if the bricks were arranged along octagonal rings, they would form angles in correspondence to the joints between two adjacent webs on the plane of the bricklaying bed.

Thus, discontinuities in the structure would arise precisely at those points where the greatest concentrations of stresses oc-

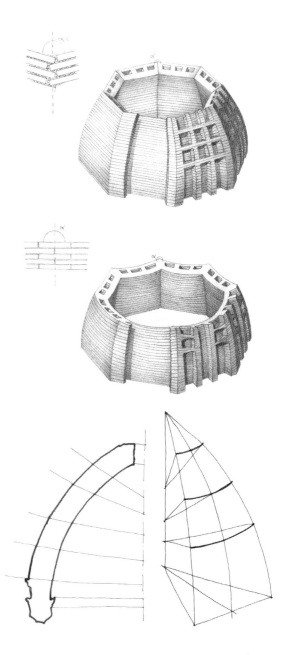

cur. Such an arrangement would cause some very serious damage, with dangerous consequences for the Dome's stability, perhaps even its collapse. I noticed that the Cupola of the Florence Baptistery (also octagonal) had been built precisely this way and, in effect, cracking occurred at the angles. However, in this case, there is no risk of collapse, because there is an outer structure sustaining the Cupola.

But my Dome had no external supporting structure to sustain it! So, to avoid these dangerous angles from forming in correspondence to the joints between two adjacent webs, I built it as if it were a circular dome. How? Simple; follow my reasoning. I laid the brick rows (also called courses) beginning at the point where two adjacent webs came together. Where these meet, they form the so-called **groin ribs**. The Dome has eight of these groins: one for the vertex of each octagon.

These are, in effect, a series of circumferential arches and make up the framework for the whole construction. For this reason they were the first to be built. On these groins

Axonometric view of the brickwork along octagonal rings
Axonometric view of the brickwork along conical surfaces
Cross-sectional and axonometric view of conical surfaces

Idealised view of the dome under construction highlighting the groin ribs

I laid the bricks of two adjacent webs on the same plane along courses in the same plane. Each of these planes is perpendicular to the corresponding groin.

In this way I avoided formation of the dangerous corners between the brick courses belonging to two adjacent webs. At this point I was forced to keep on laying the bricks so that they were always perpendicular to the meridians of the Dome, not only in correspondence to the groins, but along the webs as well.

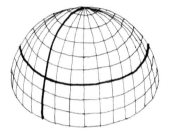

This results in the bricks being arranged along conical surfaces, just as in circular domes, remember? And this is why the brick courses in my Dome follow curved lines, called **corda blanda** (loose-rope), because they correspond to a rope which is not taut.

Therefore, the brick courses meet the meridians at right angles, just as in circular domes. The only difference being that the parallels of circular domes, which are perpendicular to the meridians, are effectively parallel to the horizontal plane of the ground.

Instead, the parallels of my Dome (that is the corda blanda) are still perpendicular to the me-

Meridians and parallels on the Earth's surface

Portion of the elliptical cylinder making up each of the dome's webs

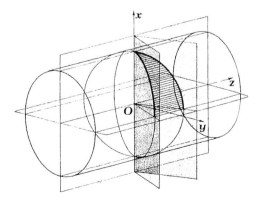

40

ridians, but do not lie on planes that are parallel to the Earth, because they run downward at first, but then run upward after reaching midway along the web. In fact, it must be borne in mind that each of the eight webs making up the Dome are not of a sphere, but of an **elliptical cylinder**.

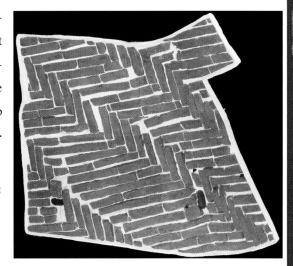

Model of the interior cupola showing the bricks under the paintings; the 'corda blanda' or dangling rope arrangement is evident

Bricks arranged according to a 'corda blanda' or dangling rope under the roof-tiles of the outer dome (Opera di Santa Maria del Fiore, stereophotographic survey of the Cupola's outer surface)

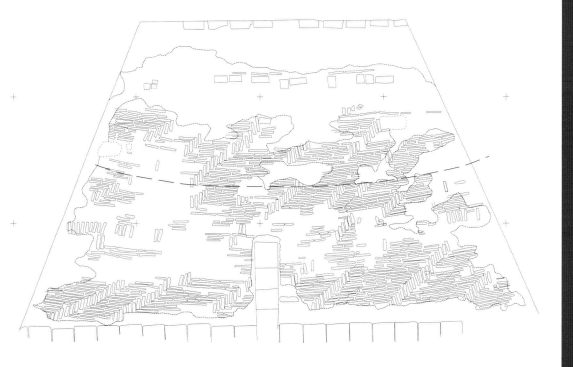

2.3

The Dome and mathematics

As I have already told you, mathematics has always been a passion of mine. There is a lot of mathematics 'hidden' in my Dome. We have already seen some of it when dealing with the herringbone and corda blanda, but there is more.

When you look at the Cupola, you will immediately perceive a sense of equilibrium and harmony amongst its various parts. Indeed, it is so, and not by chance either. The Dome's base lies upon the tambour, or drum, at almost 55 meters above the ground. The tambour itself is 13 meter in height, the Lantern is 21 meters, and the Dome is, on average, 34 meters (32 meters in the interior and 36 outside). The resulting sequence of numbers, 13, 21, 34, 55 corresponds precisely to four consecutive numbers of the renowned Fibonacci series.

Fibonacci, whose real name was Leonar-

do Pisano, was a mathematician from Pisa who lived from 1175 to 1240. Originally, Fibonacci was a merchant who in his travels came into contact with many Arab peoples. He immediately realised that their mathematics was far more advanced than Europe's. In Arab lands it was not just an abstract subject, but a very useful tool for commercial exchange. Fibonacci wrote a number of books through which he spread the Arabs' mathematical knowledge throughout Europe. In my time, many schools in Florence taught mathematics and sought to impart to future merchants and bankers those notions of arithmetic that would best serve their future activities.

Fibonacci developed this number series to resolve a problem that the famous Emperor Frederick II of Swabia had posed to him. These numbers are very important and come up again and again in many phenomena of nature and art.

They possess various noteworthy properties, one of which is that the ratio between any two consecutive Fibonacci numbers approaches the **golden number,** that is, the most harmonious relation that can be found in art or nature. This is why these relations were often used by the ancient Greeks – a people who knew something of harmony, especially in architecture.

This relation was followed not only in the Dome, but in the underlying parts of the Cathedral as well. In this regard, it should be noted that the important thing about the Dome's various elements is not their measurements in meters which, as we have seen, determine a

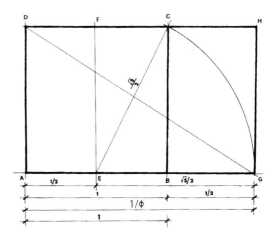

Construction of the golden rectangle

Golden proportions in the Cathedral of Santa Maria del Fiore

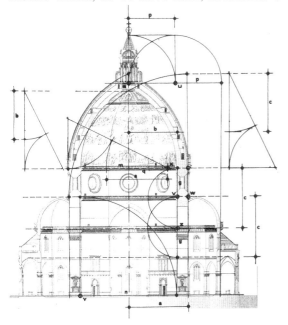

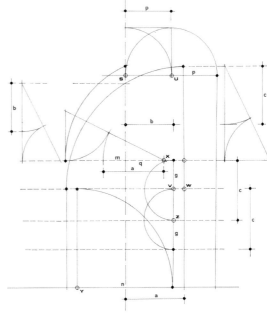

Fibonacci series (also because in my time we used to measure length in Florentine 'braccio', that is, an arm's length), but the relations amongst these elements, which do in fact approach the golden number. As you can see, mathematics can also be of great help in determining the harmony of things.

Speaking of mathematics, I would like to introduce another aspect of the Cupola. My predecessors had designed a dome with a shape that I would dare to call perfect. The curvature of the interior of the dome has a well-defined technical name, it forms an ogival arch (or **acute fifth** as I called it); that of the outer one is an **acute fourth**. Do not be alarmed by these big words; it is all very simple. Once again, we just need a bit of geometry to help explain.

We know that the inner Dome is 45 meters across at the base. If we divide it into five equal parts (hence the term 'acute fifth'), then each segment measures 9 meters. Now we place the point of a compass at the centre of the acute fifth, that is, the point 9 meters from the end, and draw a circumferential arc with a radius of 36 meters (36 = 45-9). We then re-

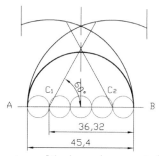

Curvature of the inner dome: acute fifth

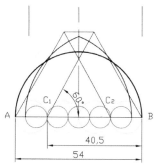

Curvature of the outer dome: acute fourth

Geometrical construction of the Dome's cross section
Catenary inscribed into the Dome's cross section

peat the same procedure centring the compass on the symmetrical point, that is, on the other centre of the acute fifth. In this way we obtain a pointed arch (i.e., an 'acute' one with a curvature whose radius is 4/5 the diameter of the base), that defines the profile of the inner Dome at the angles, that is, in correspondence to the ribs.

Using the same procedure we can trace the profile of the outer Dome as well. Its base measures 54 meters across. This time, we divide it into four equal parts (hence the term 'acute fourth') yielding segments measuring 13.5 meters each. Placing the compass in the same centres of the acute fifth that we determined before, we draw two round arches of radius 40.5 meters (40.5 = 54-13.5).

The profile of the Dome defines a shape that is extremely important for the structure's stability. In fact, its profile closely approximates an arch whose curve is called a 'catenary'. This name comes from the fact that it is the upside shape assumed by a cord hanging freely from two fixed ends.

As mathematicians would demonstrate almost three centuries later, the catenary is the

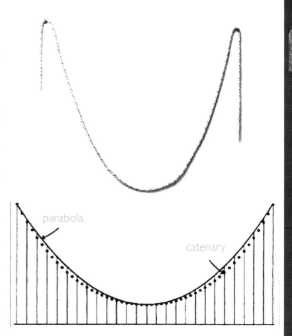

parabola

catenary

Curved catenary defined by a hanging cord
Comparison between a catenary and a parabola
Prospect of the Manhattan bridge

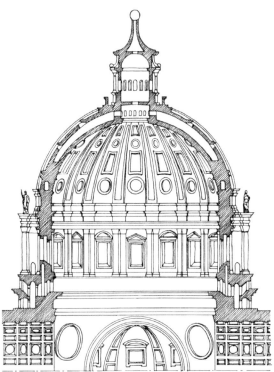

optimum shape for an arch to sustain its own weight. In the event that the so-called 'cord' bears a uniform load (as in the case of the cables holding up a suspension bridge), it then takes on a special curved shape, called a **parabola**. Spherical domes do not possess this noteworthy property. The dome of the Pantheon for instance, needs base reinforcements to counter the forces directed towards the outside in order to keep it from opening, just like a squeezed orange (as Leonardo da Vinci put it). The same phenomenon occurred in the dome of Saint Sophia in Byzantium (nowadays know as Istanbul).

The dome of Saint Peter's, which was built almost 150 years later, does not have such a perfect shape either. This cupola was erect-

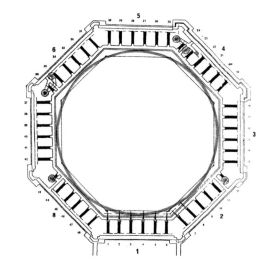

ed in only 22 months. It naturally took less time to build – it is a circular dome, and as I have already explained, this sort of structure is easier to build. It is higher than my Dome because it is set on a taller drum and it reaches a height of about 132.5 meters, while mine is, altogether, about 115 meters above the ground.

However, its base is smaller; in fact, it is about 42 meters in diameter. In practice, it is a circle inscribed into the base octagon of my Dome. Returning to the shape of the cupola of Saint Peter's: it is not so perfect. In fact, it risked collapsing due to the serious cracking that appeared in the structure. Therefore, about 150 years after its construction, five iron reinforcement rings were fitted to counter the outwards pushing forces.

My Dome, instead, had no need of such reinforcement! The damage to the dome of Saint Peter's deeply impressed the architect Christopher Wren, who at the time was building Saint Paul's Church in London. For this reason, he designed the dome of Saint Paul's in the shape of a catenary, precisely in order to avoid such shortcomings.

View of the dome of Saint Sophia in Istanbul, showing the buttresses at its base
Cross section of the dome of Saint Peter's in Rome
The base octagon of the dome of Santa Maria del Fiore with the circumference of Saint Peter's dome inscribed into it
Cross section of Saint Paul's in London showing the catenary structure

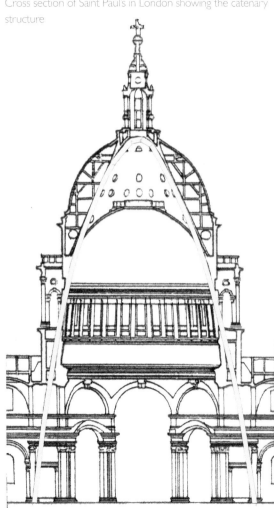

2.4
Within
the Cupola

I imagine that at this point you are curious to go up to the Cupola to have a closer look at the wonders that I have been describing to you. I shall accompany you. We can have a nice long walk and together investigate all the things I have been telling you about.

But prepare yourselves: there are 463 steps! This is no small climb. For this reason I organised the construction site in such a way that the workers did not have to keep going up and down the stairs all the time. For example, I had a platform built high up in the work area, where the cooks could prepare the food, which was then served directly to the workers up there. But first, let us enter the Cathedral: it is so big that when it was built, it was the largest church in Christendom. However, since then bigger churches have been built, so

Interior of the Cupola

Interior of the Cathedral facing the counter-façade

now it is the fourth largest in the world, after Saint Peter's in Rome, Saint Paul's in London and the Cathedral in Milan. My Dome, however, is still the largest. As I have already mentioned, the cupola of Saint Peter's has a circular base of about 42 meters in diameter, while the base (also circular) of Saint Paul's measures about 31 meters in diameter and reaches a height of 111.5 meters, and so it is also a bit lower than mine.

This small door leads to one of the four staircases that lead up to the base of the Dome; they are built directly into the enormous supporting pillars. This balcony (also called the 'gallery') that we are crossing is located at the very base of the Dome.

The 48 square holes that you can see here are the so-called 'buche pontaie' (bridge sockets), into which we inserted the main crossbeams of the framework that formed the work plane at the Dome's base.

Through this small door we can enter the Dome, finally! Time to start climbing!

The base of one of the columns with the staircase leading to the Cupola

Spiral staircase within the drum

The incline here is a bit less steep. The lower parts of the structure are made up of stone blocks to render the base stronger. Then, to keep it light, the rest was made out of bricks. We used nearly four million of them! For the same purpose of reducing the structure's weight, I built two domes: an inner one and an outer one. We are now walking in the space between the two.

If I had built a single dome, it would have been about 4.2 meters thick and far too heavy: the four supporting pillars probably would not have been able to sustain such a load.

The inner cupola, which is the one that really supports the entire structure, is about 2.20 meters thick, while the external one, whose purpose is to protect the inner one from the elements, has a thickness varying from 90 centimetres at the base to 45 centimetres at the top. An added advantage of building two separate domes was that I was able to create a passageway over a meter wide between them, to allow access to the summit. We are walking through that passage right now.

The staircase that we are ascending follows a helical curve, just like the 'herringbone' pat-

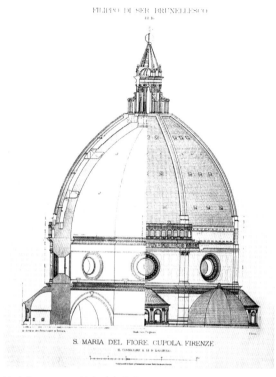

S. MARIA DEL FIORE. CUPOLA. FIRENZE

Karl Stegmann - Heinrich F. Geymüller, Cross section of the Dome showing its inner and outer shells

Horizontal section of the Dome showing the outline of the 'wooden chain'

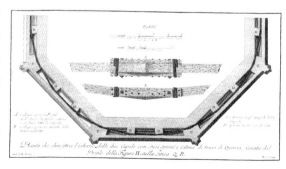

tern I told you of, but it curves in the opposite direction. Naturally, this is not by chance either: the arrangement serves to reinforce the structure. The wooden beams you see over our heads are part of a 'wooden chain' made up of 24 beams surrounding the entire dome. This ring serves to 'tighten' the Dome at the base, girding it so as to counter the dangerous forces pushing its walls outward.

Construction of this chain was a small marvel of engineering. I must say that my knowledge of mechanics and materials science came in quite useful in executing it. Its constituent beams are connected by a rather complex system of iron brackets and hinges, and its assembly was quite problematic, I assure you. And moreover, it was the key to getting my revenge on Lorenzo Ghiberti. You see, I decided to fall ill precisely when the work of assembling this chain began, leaving the task to Lorenzo, who naturally had no idea of how to manage it!

By the way, do notice the brick rows here:

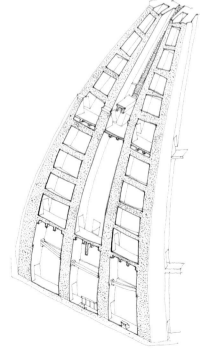

Detail of the 'wooden chain'

Detail of one of the groin ribs

Section of a Dome web showing two groin and two intermediate ribs

these form the rib, that is, the joint between these two adjacent webs of the Dome.

As we go up, you'll see the intermediate ribs as well: there are two for each web and serve to strengthen the structure.

Altogether there are 24 ribs (8 groin ribs and 16 intermediate ones) that wrap round the entire structure.

As you can see, the brick rows forming the ribs slope more and more as we approach the summit, where their inclination reaches 60° from the horizontal. The groin and intermediate ribs are connected by a series of arches (nine per web) that serve to link the outer webs with the inner ones and 'unload' the external web structures, that is, they transfer the loads onto their corresponding inner segments.

As we head up, observe the inner web on your right and outer web on your left.

You can see the various brick patterns. Some follow a curved line (the 'corda blanda', I spoke of), which runs downward and then

The arches linking the groin ribs to the intermediate ribs

The intermediate staircase joining the first and the second passageways

View within the third passageway showing the inclined bricks making up a groin rib

rises again after the middle of the web. Other bricks are set vertically: this forms the so-called 'herringbone' pattern. We are getting close to the top of the Cupola now: we are in the third passageway. See how tilted the bricks of the ribs are.

Now, let's take the staircase that lies over the inner web. Beneath our feet, there are 2.20 meters of masonry, then a drop of almost 90 meters to the Cathedral floor!

At last we have arrived at the top of the Cupola, just under the base of the Lantern, on what is called the **serraglio**, meaning closure because it 'closes' the dome (in English it is called the **apex stone**). I designed the Lantern too, but to build it I had to win another competition, which was held in 1436. At the time, I made a wooden model of the Lantern, which is still in the Museum of the *Opera del Duomo*.

Construction of the Lantern began in 1446, the year of my death. So you see, unfortunately, I never lived to see it completed. My stepson, known as Il Buggiano, supervised the operations. Luckily, he followed my design to the letter, because it plays an important role

View of the Cupola of Santa Maria del Fiore by night

Axonometric view of the bricks laid in a herringbone pattern

in the static functioning of the Cupola itself. The groin ribs converge toward the closing apex stone, which is about 6 meters in diameter. Although I had tried to make the Dome a light as possible, the forces acting on it are so great that even the strong groin ribs have a tendency to bend outwards. The lantern, with its enormous weight (about 750 tons), has the function of opposing these forces, acting as a wedge on the structure. So it bears down on the Dome through a wedge structure, which is none other than this apex stone.

Therefore, the enormous weight of the Lantern does not weaken the Dome but, to the contrary, stabilises it. As you can see, nothing was left to chance: every element of the Dome has a well thought-out function!

Let us go outside from the base of the Lantern. What a sight! From here you can admire some of the most unique architecture in all the world, some of which I built or designed myself. Here look, there is the Church of San Lorenzo, and there the Church of Santo Spirito, the Rotonda degli Angeli and Palazzo Pitti, and so many, many other masterpieces. Now, was this not worth the effort?

View of the staircase leading to the Lantern's base
Axonometric view of the apex stone at the Lantern's base
Views of Florence from atop Brunelleschi's Dome

Biography of Filippo Brunelleschi

1377 - Filippo Brunelleschi is born in Florence, the son of the notary, Ser Brunellesco di Lippo Lapi, ambassador of the Florentine Republic.

1401 - He competes in the contest for the commission to execute the second bronze door of the Florence Baptistery, for which he executes the panel illustrating *The Sacrifice of Isaac*, now in the Bargello Museum.

1402 - He goes on the first of many journeys to Rome.

1404 - He serves on the advisory board formed to buttress the Cathedral apse, and joins the Arte della Seta (Silk Guild) as a goldsmith.

1408 - He begins the marble statue of St Peter in the Church of Orsanmichele (completed in 1413). Once attributed to Donatello, the statue was only recently recognised to be Brunelleschi's work.

1409 - Together with Donatello, he arranges the prank on the "fat jack".

1412 - He travels to Prato as a consultant for construction of the Cathedral façade.

1418 - He designs the Barbadori Chapel, in the Church of Santa Felicita and the Schiatta-Ridolfi Chapel in the Church of San Jacopo Sopr'Arno.

The contest for the Cathedral Dome is held and the jurors judge Brunelleschi and Ghiberti's designs to have equal merit.

1419 - Work begins on the Ospedale degli Innocenti (Foundling Hospital), designed by Brunelleschi.

1420 - In April, Brunelleschi and Ghiberti, together with Battista d'Antonio, are named supervisors of the Dome, for which they draft the first work report. Construction begins in August. He executes the *Crucifix* for the Gondi Chapel in Santa Maria Novella, his only polychrome wood sculpture.

1421 - He drafts the preliminary design for the Church of San Lorenzo.

1422 - He begins construction of the Old Sacristy of San Lorenzo.

1424 - Brunelleschi supervises operations on the Pistoia Hospital. He then journeys to Pisa to work on its fortifications. He also works on the city walls of Lastra a Signa and Malmantile, both still visible today.

1425 - He supervises operations on the main floor of Palazzo di "Parte Guelfa" as well as on the Church of San Lorenzo.

1426 - He drafts the second report for the Cupola's construction.

1427 - He collaborates on the perspective layout of Masaccio's fresco of the *Trinità* (*Holy Trinity*) in Santa Maria Novella.

1429 - He begins construction of the Pazzi Chapel in the Church complex of Santa Croce and designs the Church of Santo Spirito.

1430 - Brunelleschi travels to Lucca to provide military advice to the Florentine army besieging the city. He designs Palazzo Busini-Bardi.

1431 - Brunelleschi supervises alterations to the fortresses of Rendine, Staggia and Castellina.

1432 - He travels to Mantua and Ferrara, probably to provide military advice. He drafts the preliminary design of the Dome Lantern.

1434 - He designs the Rotunda di Santa Maria degli Angeli, which was never to be completed.

1435 - He travels to Rimini to see Sigismondo Malatesta

1436 - The dome is completed. Brunelleschi inspects the fortifications of Pisa and Vicopisano and is awarded the commission for the Lantern.

1438 - He designs the 'Tribune morte' in Santa Maria del Fiore.

1444 - Brunelleschi is sent to Pisa to reinforce the banks of the Arno and begins construction of the Church of Santo Spirito.

1446 - Brunelleschi dies during the night of April 15 to 16.

Glossary of the Cupola

The entries marked with * are illustrated in the glossary

*Acute fourth and fifth. *Terms once used to indicate the geometric profile of particular pointed (acute) arches (also called ogival or lancet arches). They refer to two round (or circular) arches that have their centres at different symmetrical points along the diameter of a dome's base. In the case of the acute fifth, the radius of the arches are 4/5 the diameter of the impost, while for the acute fourth this ratio is 3/4.*

Brackets or **stirrups.** *Metal bars used to fasten stone or brick structures together.*

Centring. *A construction technique that uses a temporary, usually wooden framework (centred framework) to define the geometry of an arch or vault and support the structure during its construction (until it is self-supporting).*

*Circular or **rotating dome.** *A dome whose base is a circle. Its geometric shape is obtained by rotating a curve around an axis, called the axis of rotation. The curve that generates a circular dome determines its meridians. The simplest example of a circular dome is hemispherical, obtained by rotating one quarter of the circumference.*

Cone. *In mathematics, the surface traced by moving a straight line (the generatrix) along the points of a curve (the directrix), while the other end remains fixed at a point (the vertex).*

Corda blanda. *'Loose-rope', Curved pattern of brick courses in which the rows of bricks curve downward from one rib until they reach the middle of the web; then slope back up along the web until they reach the next rib. Thus, it gives the impression of a festoon or a chord dangling loosely between two fixed ends (the ribs).*

Cylinder. *In mathematics, the surface traced by moving a straight line (the generatrix) along the points of a curve (the directrix), while the line remains parallel to a fixed direction. If the directrix is a circumference lying on a plane perpendicular to the fixed direction, the cylinder is termed a **circular cylinder**. If the directrix is instead an ellipse lying on a plane perpendicular to the fixed direction, it is an **elliptical cylinder**.*

*Cylindrical helix. *A space curve that is the locus of a point moving along the surface of a cylinder so that it makes a constant angle with cross sections of the cylinder. A spiral staircase is the simplest example of a cylindrical helix.*

Dome. *An architectural term often used*

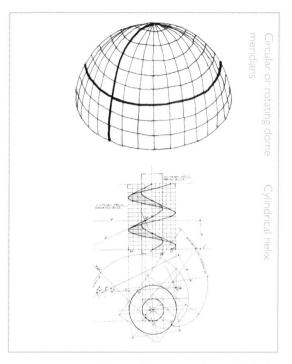

Circular or rotating dome
meridians

Cylindrical helix

synonymously with cupola. Strictly speaking it signifies the external part of a spherical or polygonal covering of a building, of which the cupola is the inner structure, but in general usage dome means the entire covering.

Drum or **tambour.** *A masonry structure used to support a dome. It may be cylindrical or polygonal in shape (Brunelleschi's is octagonal). Its sides contain small windows, called **'lunettes'**.*

Fibonacci series. *In mathematics, a series of numbers obtained in the following way: the* first number of the series is 0, the second is 1, and the subsequent numbers are the sum of the previous two. Accordingly, the Fibonacci series is: 0, 1, 1, 2, 3, 5, 8, 13, 21, 34, 55, 89, 144, 233…

*Golden number. *Also indicated by the Greek letter 'φ' (fi). Its exact numerical value is $\frac{\sqrt{5}-1}{2}$, or approximately 0.618. This number defines the relation between the height of a golden (i.e., aesthetically perfect) rectangle and its base. This number occurs extensively in the relations between objects in art and nature.*

Groin ribs. *Masonry structures originating at the vertices of the octagonal base of a dome and converging upward toward its summit (the apex stone at the base of the lantern). These ribs define circular arches. From the dome's exterior they are clearly recognisable by the white marble covering them.*

Herringbone pattern. *Brick laying technique used in Brunelleschi's dome. It calls for laying some rows vertically (knife-edged) so as to block the bricks of the "corda blanda", which are instead laid flat. This arrangement (also called a soldier course) keeps the flat bricks from slipping off during construction of the upper portions of the dome where the bricks are heavily inclined.*

Lantern. *The structure crowning a dome. It*

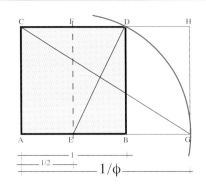

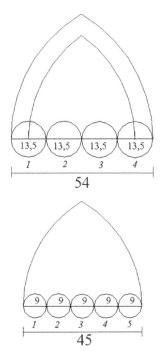

serves to allow light to enter the church. However, the white marble lantern in Brunelleschi's dome also plays an important role in its static equilibrium.

*Meridians. The lines obtained by intersecting a dome with the planes passing through its axis. The groin ribs of the dome are a particular kind of meridian. In circular domes, the meridians are all arcs of a circle. In Brunelleschi's dome only the meridians formed by the groin ribs are arcs of a circle; the intermediate meridians are arcs of an ellipse.

Parallel. The circumference of a circular dome obtained by intersecting it with planes perpendicular to its axis of rotation.

Parabola. In mathematics, a special type of curve often encountered in nature. For instance, the trajectory taken by an object thrown into the air is a parabola, as is the curve followed by the cables holding up a suspension bridge. The so-called 'dish antenna' and the headlamps of an automobile are parabolic surfaces generated by an arc of a parabola rotating around its axis of symmetry.

Scaffolding. Temporary wood and/or metal structures which form platforms for workers and materials during construction of a building. For Brunelleschi's dome a fixed scaffolding was set up at a height of about 54 meters above ground, that is, at the cupola's base. This was supported by large beams insert into expressly made holes in the walls (i.e., 'buche pontaie' or bridge sockets). Further up, they presumably used mobile scaffolding, supported by the masonry that had already been completed.

Serraglio or **apex stone.** A masonry structure positioned where the dome 'closes' (hence its name meaning (en)closure), at the apex. It is shaped like a truncated octagonal pyramid, with its base upward. It also serves as the base of the lantern.

Vault. This is a construction method for roofing buildings. The simplest form, the barrel vault, is a series of semicircular arches placed one next to the other to form a barrel-like roof. Other types include groin(ed), cross, cloister and ribbed vaults. Brunelleschi's dome can be considered a cloister vault with octagonal base.

Web or **cell.** One of the segments making up a non-circular dome. Since Brunelleschi's dome is a double shell, there are eight inner webs and eight outer ones. These latter are easily recognisable from the outside by the groin ribs separating them.

Bibliography

Bartoli L., *Il disegno della cupola del Brunelleschi*, Olschki, Florence 1994.

Battisti E., *Filippo Brunelleschi*, Electa, Milan 1989.

Dalla Negra R., edited by, *La Cupola di Santa Maria del Fiore. Il rilievo fotogrammetrico*, Sillabe, Livorno 2004.

Di Pasquale S., *La costruzione della cupola di Santa Maria del Fiore*, Biblioteca Marsilio, Venice 2002.

Eusepi S. - Grisanti G., *Il Duomo Nuovo di Siena. Vicende costruttive dal 1339 al 1357*, degree thesis, prof. Gastone Petrini, 1999-2000, Faculty of Architecture, University of Florence

Fabriczy C., *Filippo Brunelleschi. La vita e le opere*, edited by A. M. Poma, Uniedit, Florence 1977.

Fanelli G., *Brunelleschi*, Becocci-Scala, Florence 1977.

Fanelli G., Fanelli M., *La Cupola del Brunelleschi. Storia e futuro di una grande struttura*, Mandragora, Florence 2004.

Guasti C., *La Cupola di Santa Maria del Fiore illustrata con i documenti dell'Archivio dell'Opera secolare*, Barbera Bianchi e Comp., Firenze 1857, anastatic reprint A. Forni, Bologna 1974.

Gurrieri F., *La cupola*, in F. Gurrieri, G. Belli, A. Benvenuti Papi, R. Dalla Negra, P. Fabbri, V. Tesi, *La cattedrale di Santa Maria del Fiore a Firenze*, I, Florence 1994.

King R., *La cupola di Brunelleschi*, Rizzoli, Milan 2001.

Ippolito L., Peroni C., *La cupola di Santa Maria del Fiore*, La Nuova Italia Scientifica, Rome 1997.

Livio M., *La sezione aurea*, Rizzoli, Milan 2003.

Mainstone R. J., *Brunelleschi's Dome of S. Maria del Fiore and some related structures*, London 1970.

Manetti A., *Vita di Filippo Brunelleschi*, edited by C. Perrone, Salerno Editrice, Rome 1992.

Nardini Despotti Mospignotti A., *Filippo di Ser Brunellesco e la Cupola del Duomo di Firenze*, dalla Tipografia di Giuseppe Meucci, Livorno 1885.

Ragghianti L. C., *Filippo Brunelleschi. Un uomo, un universo*, Vallecchi, Florence 1977.

Rossi P. A., *Principi costruttivi nella Cupola di Santa Maria del Fiore*, in "La critica d'Arte", XLIII, 1978, pp. 93-94.

Saalman H., *Filippo Brunelleschi. The cupola of Santa Maria del Fiore*, A. Zwemmer, London 1980.

Sanpaolesi P., *Brunelleschi*, Edizioni per il Club del Libro, Milan 1962.

Sanpaolesi P., *La cupola di Santa Maria del Fiore: il progetto, la costruzione*, Edam, Florence 1977.

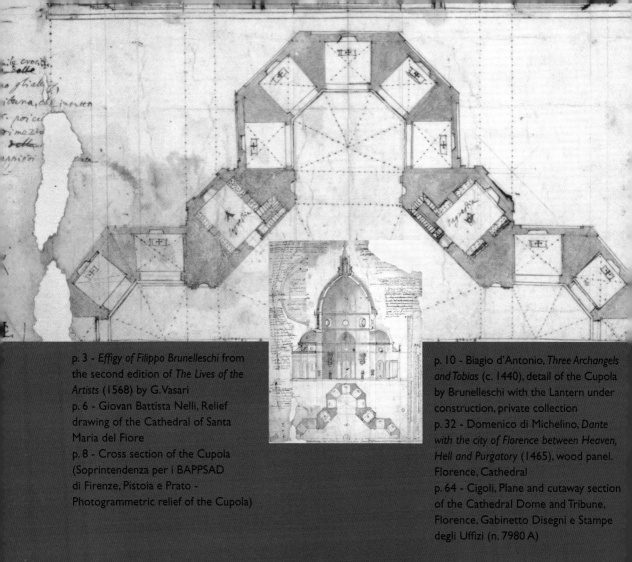

p. 3 - *Effigy of Filippo Brunelleschi* from the second edition of *The Lives of the Artists* (1568) by G. Vasari

p. 6 - Giovan Battista Nelli, Relief drawing of the Cathedral of Santa Maria del Fiore

p. 8 - Cross section of the Cupola (Soprintendenza per i BAPPSAD di Firenze, Pistoia e Prato - Photogrammetric relief of the Cupola)

p. 10 - Biagio d'Antonio, *Three Archangels and Tobias* (c. 1440), detail of the Cupola by Brunelleschi with the Lantern under construction, private collection

p. 32 - Domenico di Michelino, *Dante with the city of Florence between Heaven, Hell and Purgatory* (1465), wood panel. Florence, Cathedral

p. 64 - Cigoli, Plane and cutaway section of the Cathedral Dome and Tribune, Florence, Gabinetto Disegni e Stampe degli Uffizi (n. 7980 A)

printed in February 2005

by Genesi

Città di Catello for

s i l l a b e